Shadow Play

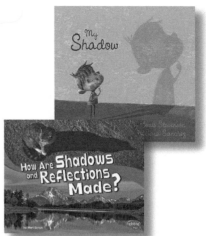

Description

Students explore the phenomenon of shadows. They listen to a classic poem about shadows, create shadows with flashlights and figurines, and change shadows by moving a light source. They read a nonfiction book that explains how shadows are made and then test different materials to see which would be best for making shadow puppets.

Alignment With the *Next Generation Science Standards*

Performance Expectation
1-PS4-3: Plan and conduct an investigation to determine the effect of placing objects made with different materials in the path of a beam of light.

Science and Engineering Practices	Disciplinary Core Idea	Crosscutting Concept
Planning and Carrying Out Investigations Plan and conduct investigations collaboratively to produce data to serve as the basis for evidence to answer a question. **Obtaining, Evaluating, and Communicating Information** Obtain information using various texts, text features, and other media that will be useful in answering a scientific question and/or supporting a scientific claim.	**PS4.B: Electromagnetic Radiation** Some materials allow light to pass through them, others allow only some light through, and others block all the light and create a dark shadow on any surface beyond them, where the light cannot reach. Mirrors can be used to redirect a light beam.	**Cause and Effect** Simple tests can be designed to gather evidence to support or refute student ideas about causes.

Note: The activities in this lesson will help students move toward the performance expectations listed, which is the goal after multiple activities. However, the activities will not by themselves be sufficient to reach the performance expectations.

Featured Picture Books

TITLE: *My Shadow*
AUTHOR: **Robert Louis Stevenson**
ILLUSTRATOR: **Sarah Sanchez**
PUBLISHER: **First Sky Pony Press**
YEAR: **2016**
GENRE: **Poetry**
SUMMARY: *Illustrator Sara Sanchez's whimsical paintings accompany Robert Louis Stevenson's classic poem.*

TITLE: *How Are Shadows and Reflections Made?*
AUTHOR: **Mari Schuh**
PUBLISHER: **Capstone**
YEAR: **2020**
GENRE: **Non-Narrative Information**
SUMMARY: *Simple text and photographs describe what happens when light hits different objects.*

Time Needed

This lesson will take several class periods. Suggested scheduling is as follows:

Session 1: **Engage** with *My Shadow* Read-Aloud

Session 2: **Explore** with Shadow Challenges

Session 3: **Explain** with *How Are Shadows and Reflections Made?* Read-Aloud

Session 4: **Elaborate** with Will Light Pass Through? Investigation

Session 5: **Evaluate** with Shadow Play

Materials

For Shadow Challenges (per pair)

- Flashlight
- Small toy figurine

For Will Light Pass Through? Investigation (per group of 4)

- Flashlight
- 4" × 4" squares of a variety of materials to test that are transparent, translucent, and opaque
  Transparent:
  - Plastic zipper bag
  - Clear plastic bottle
  - Clear acetate or cellophane

Translucent:

- Colored plastic bottle
- Wax paper
- Tissue paper
- Gauze
- Sheer fabric
- Colored acetate or cellophane
- Paper towel
- Plastic grocery bag

Opaque:

- Cardstock
- Construction paper
- Copy paper
- Cardboard
- Aluminum foil
- Felt
- Paper bag

For Shadow Play

- Wooden skewers with sharp tips cut off, wooden chopsticks, or craft sticks
- Tape
- Cardstock
- Shadow Puppet Cutouts copied on cardstock
- *Optional:* Cardboard boxes and parchment paper or white poster paper to create a shadow stage for each group

Student Pages

- Shadow Puppet Cutouts
- Shadow Play
- STEM Everywhere

Background for Teachers

Light is a form of energy that travels from a source in a straight line until it hits something. Some materials allow light to pass straight through them. These are called *transparent* materials. Windows, clear plastic wrap, and air are transparent. When light encounters transparent materials, almost all of the light comes through. For example, glass allows all visible light through. This is why we can see through glass. Other materials only allow some light through. These are referred to as *translucent* materials. Frosted glass, some plastics, and tissue paper are translucent. When light hits a translucent material, the light that does come through bounces around instead of going straight through. Things look fuzzy when

looking through translucent materials. Materials that do not allow any light through are called *opaque* materials. Cardboard, wood, and metal are opaque materials. When light hits opaque materials, it is usually reflected or absorbed by the object. The area where light can't pass though is called a *shadow*.

In this lesson, students use the science and engineering practice (SEP) of planning and carrying out investigations by testing materials to see which would be best for creating puppets for a shadow play. They use the SEP of obtaining, evaluating, and communicating information as they read a nonfiction book about transparent, translucent, and opaque materials and about how shadows are created. *Note:* It is not important that students memorize the terms (*opaque, translucent,* and *transparent*). It is more important that they understand the phenomenon that "some materials allow light to pass through them, others allow only some light through, and others block all the light and create a dark shadow on any surface beyond them" (NGSS Lead States 2013, p. 10). Some language-savvy students may adopt the terms (*transparent, translucent,* and *opaque*) and use them to describe materials for the remainder of the lesson; others may want to use the phrases "lets all light through," "lets some light through," or "lets no light through." Both ways of describing these phenomena are acceptable.

The shape of a shadow is determined by the object blocking the light. However, the size and shape of the shadow can change by moving the light source in different positions. In this lesson, students explore the crosscutting concept (CCC) of cause and effect by changing the position and distance of a light source to an opaque object and observing the shadows.

All of the students' sensemaking about light and shadows comes together as they create a shadow play. They justify the materials they choose to make the shadow puppets based on the effect of a beam of light from a flashlight hitting the material.

Learning Progressions

Below are the disciplinary core idea (DCI) grade band endpoints for grades K–2 and 3–5. These are provided to show how student understanding of the DCIs in this lesson will progress in future grade levels.

DCIs	Grades K–2	Grades 3–5
PS4.B: Electromagnetic Radiation	• Some materials allow light to pass through them, others allow only some light through, and others block all the light and create a dark shadow on any surface beyond them, where the light cannot reach.	• An object can be seen when light reflected from its surface enters the eyes.

Source: Willard, T., ed. (2015). *The NSTA quick-reference guide to the NGSS: Elementary school.* Arlington, VA: NSTA Press.

engage

My Shadow Read-Aloud

Show students the cover of the book *My Shadow*. Tell them the text of this book was written by a famous poet, Robert Louis Stevenson, over 100 years ago! Read the book aloud. Students may giggle after the last page, which says,

> One morning, very early, before the sun was up,
>
> I rose and found the shining dew on every buttercup;
>
> But my lazy little shadow, like a naughty sleepy-head,
>
> Had stayed at home behind me and was fast asleep in bed.

This stanza is accompanied by an illustration of the shadow still in bed.

 ### Making Connections: Text to Self

After reading, *ask*

? Is it possible for your shadow to stay in bed when you go outside? (of course not!)

? What is a shadow? (Answers will vary.)

? When do you have a shadow? (Answers will vary but may include when I go outside or when I stand near a light.)

? How have you noticed your shadow changing? (Answers will vary.)

explore

Shadow Challenges

 ### Making Connections: Text to Self

Refer back to the page that reads "The funniest thing about him is the way he likes to grow," and read through that page and the six following pages that follow, ending with "And sometimes gets so little that there's none of him at all." *Ask*

? Have you ever noticed your shadow getting longer or shorter? When? Where? (Answers will vary.)

Show students a toy figurine and a flashlight. *Ask*

? How could we make this toy have a shadow? (Shine the flashlight on it.)

> **CCC: Cause and Effect**
> Simple tests can be designed to gather evidence to support or refute student ideas about causes.

Give each pair of students a flashlight and a toy figurine, and tell them that you would like them to explore with these items to see how they can change the toy's shadow. Write the following shadow challenges on the board. Read each question aloud and then give students a few minutes to explore the question with their flashlights and figurines. They can make shadows on the table where the figurine is placed. This activity will work best if the lights in the room are dimmed.

1. Can you make the shadow longer?

2. Can you make the shadow shorter?

3. Can you change the direction of the shadow?

4. What other ways can you change the shadow?

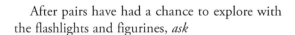

MAKING THE SHADOW LONGER

MAKING THE SHADOW SHORTER

After pairs have had a chance to explore with the flashlights and figurines, *ask*

? What did you notice about shadows as you explored? (Answers will vary, but students may have noticed that changing the position of the flashlight changed the size and shape of the shadow.)

? How can you change the direction of the shadow? (Move the flashlight to the other side of the figurine.)

? How can you make a shadow longer? (Move the flashlight to the side of the figurine.)

? How can you make the shadow shorter? (Move the flashlight above the figurine.)

? How else did you change the shadow? (Invite pairs of students to demonstrate various ways they changed the shadow of the figurine.)

? What are you wondering about shadows?

Making Connections: Text to World

Revisit the illustrations from *My Shadow* and observe the size of the boy's shadows and the location of the light source. For example, when the boy's shadow is short, the light is right overhead, and when the shadow is long, the light source is to the side of the boy. Make connections with students' experience with changing the shadow of the figurine to the way the illustrator represented changing shadows in the book.

explain

How Are Shadows and Reflections Made? **Read-Aloud**

Connecting to the Common Core
Reading: Informational Text
CRAFT AND STRUCTURE: 1.5

 Features of Nonfiction

Show students the cover of *How Are Shadows and Reflections Made?* and *ask*

? From looking at the cover, do you think this book is fiction or nonfiction? (Answers will vary.)

> **SEP: Obtaining, Evaluating, and Communicating Information**
> Obtain information using various texts, text features, and other media that will be useful in answering a scientific question and/or supporting a scientific claim.

Open up the book and point out the table of contents and the glossary. Explain that these are typically features of a nonfiction book. Tell students that you want to read this book to them to answer some of their questions about shadows. Demonstrate how a table of contents can direct you right to the information you are looking for. Read the titles of the different sections listed in the table of contents. *Ask*

? Which section should we read to find out more about shadows? (Shadows and Light)

? On what page does that section begin? (page 8)

Connecting to the Common Core
Reading: Informational Text
CRAFT AND STRUCTURE: 1.4

 Questioning

Read pages 8–12 aloud and *ask*

? How is a shadow made? (Light is blocked.)

? What do we call objects that block light? (opaque)

? Was the figurine we used earlier *opaque*? (Yes, it blocked the light.)

? What other things are opaque? (Answers will vary.)

Read page 14 aloud and point out the balloon in the photograph on page 15 as an example of an object that is *translucent*. It lets some light through, but not all. *Ask*

? What are some other examples of objects that are translucent? (a plastic grocery bag, some plastic containers, a tissue, etc.)

Read page 16 aloud and point out the window in the photograph on page 17 as an example of an object that is transparent. It lets all the light through. *Ask*

? What are some other examples of things that are transparent? (eye glasses, clear jars, etc.)

Note: It is not so important that students memorize the terms (*opaque, translucent,* and *transparent*). It is more important that they understand the phenomenon that "some materials allow light to pass through them, others allow only some light through, and others block all the light and create a dark shadow on any surface beyond them" (NGSS Lead States 2013, p. 10). Some language-savvy students may adopt the terms (*transparent, translucent,* and *opaque*) and use them to describe materials for the remainder of the lesson; others may want to use the phrases "lets all light through," "lets some light

through," or "lets no light through." Both ways of describing these phenomena are acceptable.

Read pages 18–21 aloud and *ask*

? What does "reflect" mean? (bouncing off)

? What happens when an object reflects light? (We can see it.)

? What kinds of objects reflect a lot of light? (Shiny objects like the pan on page 19 and mirrors, like the one on page 21.

Reiterate to students that shiny objects are not the only things that reflect light; actually, everything they can see reflects light. That's how we are able to see it. Without light, we would not be able to see ANYTHING!

elaborate

Will Light Pass Through? Investigation

Ask

? Have you ever seen a shadow play or a shadow puppet? (Answers will vary.)

Tell students that you have a video of a shadow puppet show to share. Start the video "How to Make Shadow Puppets" from Full-Time Kid on PBS at 52 seconds so that it starts right when the shadow puppet show begins. (Students will watch the beginning of the video about how the puppets were made later, after they have a chance to experiment with different materials. The video is listed in the "Website" section at the end of this lesson.)

After watching, *ask*

? What materials do you think were used to make the shadow puppets? (Answers will vary.)

? Why do you think the artist used those materials? (Answers will vary.)

? Do you think it is possible to use other materials to make shadow puppets? (Answers will vary.)

Divide students into groups of four and give them 4" × 4" squares of a variety of materials that are transparent, translucent, and opaque (see Materials list). *Ask*

? Which of these materials do you think could be used to make shadow puppets? (Answers will vary.)

? What kinds of materials make shadows? (Materials that don't let light pass through.)

Turn and Talk

> **SEP: Planning and Carrying Out Investigations**
> Plan and conduct investigations collaboratively to produce data to serve as the basis for evidence to answer a question.

Ask

? How could we test these materials to see which ones do not let light pass through?

Give groups a chance to brainstorm ideas with each other and then have them share their ideas with the class. Work together to design an investigation where they can test materials and classify them into three categories:

- All light passes through (transparent)
- Some light passes through (translucent)
- No light passes through (opaque)

An investigation might look something like this:

1. Shine a flashlight on the wall.
2. Hold each material in front of a flashlight.
3. Observe whether or not the material lets light through.
4. Record which category it fits in: lets all light through, lets some light through, or lets no light through.
5. Record the results on a class chart or simply create three piles—one for each category.

Note: This test works best if students hold the material about 6 inches away from the flashlight.

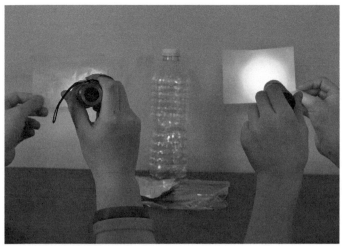

TESTING THE MATERIALS

Answers for the materials included in this lesson are in the chart below.

> **CCC: Cause and Effect**
> Simple tests can be designed to gather evidence to support or refute student ideas about causes.

After students have determined which category each material belongs in, *ask*

? Would all of the materials in the "no light passes through" (opaque) category make good shadow puppets? (No, some of them are not sturdy, like the aluminum foil.)

? Which material do you think would be best for making the shadow puppets? (Answers will vary, but the best choice would be a material that is sturdy and does not let light through—opaque.)

evaluate

Shadow Play

Optional: Ahead of time, prepare a stage box for each group of four to six students. If you don't have the time or materials to create the stage boxes, a blank, flat wall or white poster paper will do just fine.

Tell students they are going to get to create and perform their own shadow puppet play! Show students the beginning of the video "How to Make Shadow Puppets" from Full-Time Kid on PBS that shows how the puppets were made (see the "Website" section).

After watching, *ask*

? What materials did the girl in the video use to make the shadow puppets? (cardstock and skewers)

Transparent	Translucent	Opaque
ALL light passes through	SOME light passes through	NO light passes through
• Clear acetate or cellophane	• Colored acetate or cellophane	• Aluminum foil
• Clear plastic bottle	• Colored plastic bottle	• Cardboard
• Plastic zipper bag	• Gauze	• Cardstock
	• Paper towel	• Construction paper
	• Plastic grocery bag	• Copy paper
	• Sheer fabric	• Felt
	• Tissue paper	• Paper bag
	• Wax paper	

? Why do you think she used those materials? (The skewers are thin and straight to hold up the puppets; cardstock keeps its shape and does not let light pass through.)

? Why do you think the girl covered the open end of the box with parchment paper? (to make a background for the shadows)

There are several different ways to do the shadow puppet plays—you can have students use the templates provided (the Shadow Puppet Cutouts student pages) to create their play, they can come up with their own puppets, or they can use both the templates and their own creations. If you use the Shadow Puppet Cutouts, be sure to have them copied on cardstock ahead of time. If you want to allow for even more creativity (and you have time) you could allow students to use other materials from the Will Light Pass Through? investigation. For example, students could use the copy paper to make "hair" on their cut outs. Who knows what creative ideas they will come up with! You could also extend this part of the lesson into a language arts lesson about story elements.

As students come up with a story, have them discuss how they will tell the story using their puppets:

? Who are the story characters?

? Does your story have a beginning, a middle, and an end?

? What will the puppets say and do?

As you visit groups as they are working on their plays, remind them of the activity they did with the figurine in the *explore* phase of the lesson. They could change the size of the shadow by changing the distance the object is from the flashlight.

Connecting to the Common Core
Writing
RESEARCH TO BUILD KNOWLEDGE: K.8

SHADOW PLAY

When students are finished coming up with their play and puppets and are ready to perform, give each student a copy of the Shadow Play student page. Have them write the title of the play, list the materials they used, and explain why they used those materials.

STEM Everywhere

Give students the STEM Everywhere student page as a way to involve their families and extend their learning. They can do the activity with an adult helper and share their results with the class. If students do not have access to the internet at home, you may choose to have them complete this activity at school.

Opportunities for Differentiated Instruction

This box lists questions and challenges related to the lesson that students may select to research, investigate, or innovate. Students may also use the questions as examples to help them generate their own questions. These questions can help you move your students from the teacher-directed investigation to engaging in the science and engineering practices in a more student-directed format.

Extra Support

For students who are struggling to meet the lesson objectives, provide a question and guide them in the process of collecting research or helping them design procedures or solutions.

Extensions

For students with high interest or who have already met the lesson objectives, have them choose a question (or pose their own question), conduct their own research, and design their own procedures or solutions.

After selecting one of the questions in this box or formulating their own questions, students can individually or collaboratively make predictions, design investigations or surveys to test their predictions, collect evidence, devise explanations, design solutions, or examine related resources. They can communicate their findings through a science notebook, at a poster session or gallery walk, or by producing a media project.

Research

Have students brainstorm researchable questions:

? What are some natural light sources and some human-made light sources? Make a T-chart.

? How does a sundial work?

? Look for some shadows on the playground. How do the shadows compare with the shape and size of the objects making the shadows?

Investigate

Have students brainstorm testable questions to be solved through science or math:

? What happens when light passes through water? Place an object (like a pencil) in a clear container full of water. How does the appearance of the object change?

? How does your shadow change from morning, to noon, to afternoon on a sunny day? Have a friend trace your shadow at each time of day with sidewalk chalk to find out.

? What is the temperature of a surface within a shadow compared to the temperature of the same surface in the sunshine?

Innovate

Have students brainstorm problems to be solved through engineering:

? Can you and your friends use your shadows to create a picture or a scene? Try it on a sunny day and take a photo of your creation.

? Can you design a game where your friends guess the object by the shadow it makes?

? Can you use LEGOs or blocks to create interesting shadows?

Website

"How to Make Shadow Puppets" video from Full-Time Kid on PBS
www.sdpb.org/blogs/children-and-education/full-time-kid-how-to-make-shadow-puppets

More Books to Read

Asch, F. 2014. *Moonbear's shadow.* New York: Aladdin.
Summary: In this reissue of a cherished classic, Moonbear tries to outsmart his shadow.

Leathers, P. 2016. *The black rabbit.* Somerville, MA: Candlewick Press.
Summary: Rabbit sees a big black rabbit chasing him wherever he goes. He loses the big black rabbit in the dark woods, only to find him again when he goes out into the sunshine. The reader is in on the secret that the black rabbit is just Rabbit's shadow, which makes for a humorous tale.

Bulla, C. R. 1994. *What makes a shadow?* New York: HarperCollins.
Summary: This Let's-Read-and-Find-Out Science book gives simple explanations for shadows. Each page offers a brief description of an object and its shadow. Simple activities to demonstrate various sizes and shapes of shadows are included.

Sayre, A. P. 2002. *Shadows.* New York: Henry Holt.
Summary: A boy and girl search for shadows on a sunny summer day.

Reference

NGSS Lead States. 2013. *Next Generation Science Standards: For states, by states.* Washington, DC: National Academies Press. *www.nextgenscience.org/nextgeneration-science-standards.*

Shadow Puppet Cutouts

Shadow Puppet Cutouts cont.

Shadow Play

Name: _____

Title: _____

Materials we used (write or draw):

We used these materials because: _____

Name: _____

STEM Everywhere (Page 1)

Dear Families,

At school, we have been learning about **light and shadows**. We explored how some materials let light pass through, while other materials block light and create a shadow. To find out more, ask your learner the following questions and discuss their answers:

• What did you learn?

• What was your favorite part of the lesson?

• What are you still wondering?

 At home, you can explore shadows by making hand shadows. You need a light source, your hands, and your imagination! See the attached sheet to get some ideas for how to make shadows that look like animals, and then come up with your own hand shadow ideas. For more ideas, scan the QR code or go to *www.youtube.com/watch?v=Uv-MdaBfk8U*.

Draw and label some of the hand shadows you were able to make together.

STEM Everywhere (Page 2)

Animal-Shaped Hand Shadow Examples

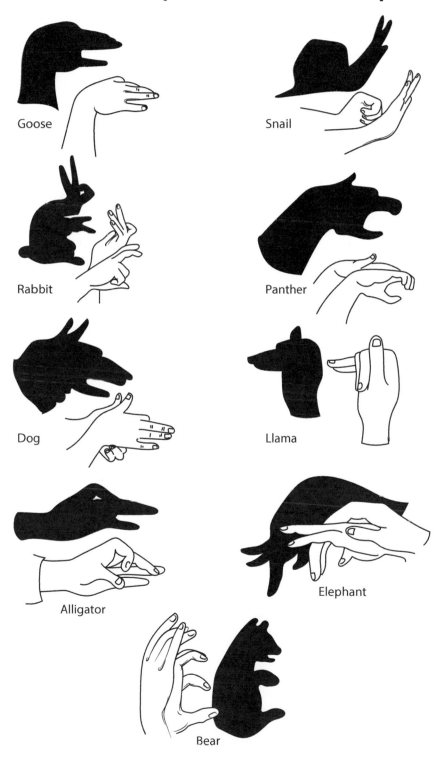

Goose

Snail

Rabbit

Panther

Dog

Llama

Alligator

Elephant

Bear